Write-and-Read Math Story Books

Reproducible Patterns for 12 Interactive Books That Build Early Math and Reading Skills

by Betsy Franco

SCHOLASTIC

PROFESSIONAL BOOKS

New York ✤ Toronto ✤ London ✤ Auckland ✤ Sydney ✤ Mexico City ✤ New Delhi ✤ Hong Kong

Dedication

To my seventh-grade teacher who taught us
Alice in Wonderland in math class

Cover design by Norma Ortiz

Cover photography by Donnelly Marks

Interior Design by Ellen Matlach Hassell for Boultinghouse & Boultinghouse, Inc.

Interior Illustration by Maxie Chambliss and Manuel Rivera

ISBN 0-590-98391-1

Contents

12 Write-and-Read Math Story Books

Introduction

Math mini-books work well on so many levels. Not only do they present appropriate math concepts in enjoyable contexts, but the math is embedded in a predictable text that children can read for themselves. The books are personal, the text is involving and interactive, and the children can play the role of both book author and illustrator.

Success is built into the easy format of the mini-book. Children can take pride in their ability to do the math, read the book, and share their creations with others at school and at home. With mini-books, children have a real investment in their own learning.

Teaching notes make the experience easy for you, too. The math objective is stated at the beginning of each teaching note so that you know where to fit it into your curriculum. Ideas for assessing children's prior knowledge and simple ways to introduce or review the math concepts are also included. Suggestions for making the book, sharing it with others, and extension activities are provided for each book as well.

Betsy Franco

How to Assemble and Use the Mini-Books

When introducing the mini-book, it is beneficial to create a completed sample to show the class. By reading through your book and pointing out all the steps you took, you help children feel comfortable when they create their own mini-books.

The books have been designed for ease of assembly. See the detailed instructions below. It is best to assemble the books together as a class. Of course, you might want to assemble the books yourself, depending on the time of year and the level of children.

Assembling the Books

1. Copy the pages for books on standard 8½-inch by 11-inch paper, making the pages single-sided.

2. Fold the front cover/back cover in half along the dashed line, keeping the fold to the left side.

3. Fold each inner page in half, keeping the fold to the right side.

4. Place the inner pages inside the cover and staple three times along the spine.

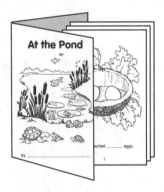

The steps children take to complete the mini-books are different for each book. This not only lends variety but also guarantees that each book format fits the particular math skill. In some books, children fill in a number or a number sentence in the text. In other books, words or sentences

are missing from the text. Children can write these in themselves, they can dictate their answers, or you can write their responses on self-stick notes and have children copy the words. In other mini-books, children draw all or part of the illustrations, using clues in the text.

Sharing the books is a major part of the process. Self-confidence and pride in learning are fostered when children share their books with partners or the class, and in class choral readings. Books can also be read to children in other classes or to buddies. Finally, children can take the books home to share their accomplishments in both math and reading with family members. A reproducible family letter appears on page 26. There is a space for family comments at the back of each mini-book. These can be shared with the class when the mini-books are returned.

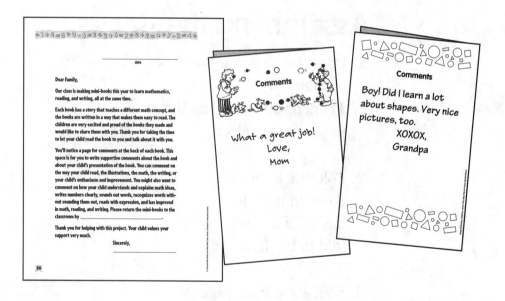

Creative suggestions for going beyond the book are also given in the teaching notes for each mini-book. Children are encouraged to reinforce their math and reading skills by making their own books and by creating class collaborative books. They can dramatize the stories, make murals or collages, or listen to other stories with similar math themes.

Success and confidence are the key words throughout the process of making mini-books. The simple, effective format lets every child become a mathematician, a writer, and an illustrator!

A Hat for Each Head

pages 28–31   ONE-TO-ONE CORRESPONDENCE

Objective

Children learn about matching and one-to-one correspondence while drawing appropriate numbers of hats for different groups of people pictured in the mini-book. They count the number of people and the number of hats to complete the text on every page.

Getting Started

Have children discuss the different types of hats they own and hats they've seen people wearing at work and at play. Possibilities are bike helmets, baseball caps, hard hats, swim caps, firefighters' helmets, and straw hats.

Present the following situation to children:

It's a very cold day. 5 children are putting on hats before they go outside for recess.

Draw the 5 children on chart paper. Ask how many hats there should be for 5 children. Let volunteers take turns drawing the hats on the children's heads on the chart paper. Emphasize that the number of children and the number of hats are the same. Present another situation in which 4 children take umbrellas outside in the rain. How many umbrellas would there be for 4 children?

Introducing the Book

Show children the sample book you made for *A Hat for Each Head*. Read aloud the first few pages and discuss the number of clowns and the number of hats you drew. Finish reading the mini-book to children. Point out the pattern in the text. Then talk about why construction workers need to wear hard hats for protection. Ask why baseball players and bicycle riders need to wear hats, too.

Making the Book

Duplicate pages 28–31 and pass out one mini-book to each child. Work together as a class to assemble the books. Make sure children understand that they are to draw the appropriate hats on the people and then write the number of hats on the blank lines. Explain to children that they can refer to the hats on the cover when making their drawings.

Sharing the Book

This book is well suited to a class choral reading. If you divide children into two groups, one group can read the first sentence on each page while the other group reads and completes the second sentence. Then the book can be reread with groups switching roles.

Send the book home for children to share with family members along with the family letter on page 26. When the books are returned, share the comments with the class.

Going Beyond the Book

Celebrate a funny hat day in which each child wears a funny hat to school. Have different groups of children come forward, and let the class talk about how many children and how many hats there are.

The Circus

pages 32–37   SIMPLE COUNTING

Objective

Children count and record the number of objects on each mini-book page. The pages are designed to present the numbers in the counting sequence in order.

Getting Started

Have children talk about what they might see at a circus. Some may respond from firsthand experience and others from circuses they have seen on television or read about in books. Ask:

> *How many rings would you see at a circus?*
> *What kinds of animals would you see?*
> *What kinds of people take part in a circus?*

You might want to read aloud some fiction and/or nonfiction books on circuses, such as *Randy's Dandy Lions* by Bill Peet (Houghton, 1964).

Introducing the Book

Display the book you made to the class. Using the first three pages as a guide, show children how you read the text, counted the tent, the tickets, and the circus rings and wrote the numbers on the blank lines. Point out the language pattern on each page: There are (number) (object).

Making the Book

Duplicate and distribute pages 32–37 of the book. Guide children through the steps of assembling their mini-books. Have them look through the book and tell you how they will know what number to put in the blank. (Each illustration gives the clue.)

Sharing the Book

Allow pairs of children to take turns reading their books to each other. Encourage them to compare the numbers they wrote on each page. Let children take home their books to share their math and reading skills with family members. Be sure to duplicate a copy of the letter on page 26 for each child to take home with the mini-books.

Going Beyond the Book

This book is structured so that it is easy to act out. You can drape a sheet over chairs or a desk to represent the circus tent and make two tickets out of paper. Blow up balloons for the clown. Use tennis balls, rubber balls, or wads of paper for the juggler's balls. As the class reads each page in unison, call on the correct number of students to come forward and act out the scene.

At the Pond

pages 38–43   COUNTING

Objective

Children count 1 to 10 objects that appear in the mini-book illustrations. They must find a method for counting that keeps them from counting the same object twice. The number of objects from one page to the next *does not* follow the counting sequence.

Getting Started

Tell children that they will use their imagination to pretend that animals can count. Ask what objects different animals might be interested in counting and record children's responses. For instance, a dog might count bones, and a chicken might count eggs.

Draw a picture of a dog with 4 bones (or use one of the children's responses). Let children count the bones along with you. In fact, you might want to circle each bone as you count it to show one way to tell which objects have already been counted. An alternative is to use cubes to represent the objects the animals are counting. As the children count the cubes, pick up and move each cube onto a sheet of paper or a mat to show an effective way to keep track of which cubes have been counted.

Introducing the Book

Explain the context—that the animals at a pond are each counting something important to them. Present and read aloud your finished mini-book as a model for the children to follow. Show children that they will need to write a numeral on the blank lines on pages 1–8. On the last two pages, tell them that they will need to draw a picture based on clues in the text.

To help children develop organized ways of counting, show them how they could circle or cross off each object they have already counted. Some children may also use the strategy of starting at the top and moving downward.

Making the Book

After duplicating and passing out pages 38–43, have children assemble their mini-books. Make sure they find the blanks they must fill in and the pages they must illustrate at the end of the book.

Sharing the Book

Read the book in unison with the class, emphasizing the number on each page. For the last two pages, ask children sitting near each other to share their illustrations. Send the books home to be shared and commented on by family members.

Going Beyond the Book

Have each child complete a page for a class collaborative book. They can pick an animal that is not depicted in the mini-book, decide what it would like to count, and illustrate the scene. Children can dictate or write sentences to go along with their pictures. Brainstorm some ideas before children get started, such as *The chimp counted 8 bananas. The elephant counted 6 peanuts. The snail counted 5 leaves.*

I Like Shapes

pages 44–49   **TWO-DIMENSIONAL SHAPES**

Objective

Children work with two-dimensional geometric shapes on several levels. They draw the shapes with and without a context.

Getting Started

The brainstorming portion of this mini-book is very important. On chart paper, let children help you draw the geometric shapes in the book (rectangle, circle, square, triangle). Then have them suggest real objects that match those shapes. Some ideas follow:

❖ rectangle: tabletop, calendar, door, poster, puzzle, book cover, flag

❖ circle: pizza, clock, tabletop, wheel, plate, magnifying glass

❖ square: picture, checkerboard, window, tabletop, floor or ceiling tile

❖ triangle: clown hat, party hat, ice cream cone, triangular flag, arrowhead

To make sure everyone can recognize the shapes, let children describe how to make ethem. See the examples below.

❖ rectangle: 4 sides, 4 corners

❖ square: 4 sides of equal length, 4 corners (Note: It is easier for children to recognize squares than to draw them.)

❖ circle: no straight lines, no corners

❖ triangle: 3 sides, 3 corners

Introducing the Book

When you prepare the right-hand pages of your sample book, you will want to draw shapes that are different sizes and that are oriented differently on the page. Show your completed book to the class. Let children see that you have drawn several of the same shapes on the left-hand page and then a picture of that shape in a real context, labeled, on the right-hand page. Spend some time on pages 9 and 10. Explain that the house should be drawn using squares and a triangle, and the car should be drawn using rectangles and circles. Point out how you labeled the shapes on the cover.

Making the Book

Lead children through the steps of assembling the mini-book. Then review the pictures that go on the left-hand and the right-hand pages. Point out that all right-hand pages have a blank space in which children write the name of the object they drew.

Sharing the Book

Let children take turns reading their books to the class and sharing the clever pictures they made of shapes in real-life contexts. Have each child display his or her favorite page in *I Like Shapes* and let everyone walk around and admire each other's work. Have children take their books home, where they can read them and show the pictures to family members.

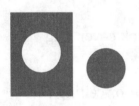

Going Beyond the Book

Provide geometric shapes that you have cut from colored paper for children to create colorful collages of objects. Their pictures can be abstract, or they can create real objects. It can be fun to let them use the cut shapes as well as paper they were cut from.

The Elves Have a Tea Party

pages 50–53   ADDITION

Objective

Children practice adding two numbers to sums of 8. First they use clues in the text to complete the pictures. Then they use the pictures and text to help them add.

Getting Started

Explain that this book is about Freddy and Franny Elf, who are preparing for a tea party. Although there are tales of "little people" in cultures all over the world, you might want to read *The Elves and the Shoemaker* or another elf tale. Then ask questions and supply information about elves:

* *How big are elves? What do they do with toadstools?* (tiny; sit under them, sit on them)

* *What do they wear?* (pointed hats, simple earth-colored clothes)

* *What do elves look like?* (thin bodies, pointed ears)

* *What creatures are often seen with them?* (butterflies)

Discuss some things that elves might need for a tea party—cups, chairs to sit on, mint leaves for the tea, flowers for decoration, and so on. To prepare for the mini-book, explain that Franny and Freddy each bring some of the mint leaves for the tea—they bring 5 mint leaves in all. Ask children to guess how many leaves Franny and Freddy each brought. Record children's responses using pictures and numerals.

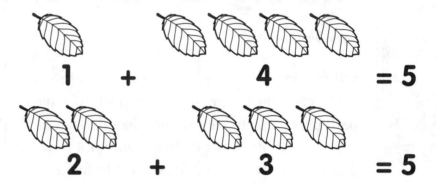

$$1 + 4 = 5$$

$$2 + 3 = 5$$

Introducing the Book

Show children the sample book you created. Read it aloud to the class. Look at pages 1 and 2 together. Let children see that you drew in Freddy's toadstools on page 2. Read the text and ask children to tell how many toadstools Freddy has. Then show how you wrote 3 + 4 = 7 on the blank line at the bottom of the page. Talk about how that number sentence means 3 toadstools + 4 toadstools = 7 toadstools. Finally, go over the last page. Ask children to find the cups, toadstools, mint leaves (in the tea), and butterflies.

Making the Book

Make copies of pages 50–53 and pass them out. Have children assemble the books. Make sure children understand that they need to complete each drawing and write a number sentence at the bottom of the page.

Sharing the Book

Have children take turns coming up to the front of the class, reading one page, and showing their colored illustrations. Send the mini-books home to be shared with family members. When children bring the books back, read some of the comments to the class.

Going Beyond the Book

Let pairs of children take turns acting out each scene in the book. The first pair can use real leaves for mint leaves. The second pair can arrange chairs or pillows to represent the toadstools, and so on. Of course, you can change the numbers in the story to extend the learning.

Making 10 with Mr. Bear

pages 54–60   SUMS OF 10

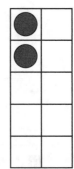

Objective

Children build the important number 10. Given partially completed ten-frames, like the one at right, in various contexts they figure out how many more spaces need to be filled to make 10.

Getting Started

Introduce or review ten-frames with children. Ten-frames are valuable because it has been shown that children can truly visualize 10 in two rows of 5. Make some flash cards showing partially completed ten-frames, or draw them on an overhead transparency. Flash the cards and have children tell how many dots they saw. Examples:

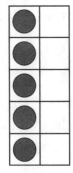 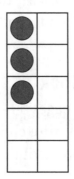 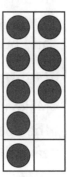

Then use the same cards and ask how many more dots are needed to make 10 in each case.

Introducing the Book

Explain that this book has a character named Mr. Bear who loves to make 10. Read your completed book to children. Point out that on page 2 Mr. Bear planted 7 flowers, and you planted (drew) 3 flowers to make 10 flowers in all. Show how you completed the number sentence on page 3.

Making the Book

Distribute copies of pages 54–60 to each child. Help children assemble the mini-books. Let them look through the books to see that they need to fill in each ten-frame, along with the blank lines on the left- and right-hand pages. Have children draw flowers in the ten-frame on the cover.

Sharing the Book

Have children read their books to partners. Also send the mini-books home so that children can share their artwork and their reading and math skills with family members.

Going Beyond the Book

Make a blackline master with a blank ten-frame on it and duplicate one ten-frame for each child. Children will need two different colors of markers or crayons. Ask each child to choose a favorite animal or object. such as rabbits or baseballs. Have them use the first color to draw the animal or object in some of the squares of the ten-frame. Then have them use the second color to draw the animal or object in the rest of the squares. Tell them to write number sentences describing what they drew.

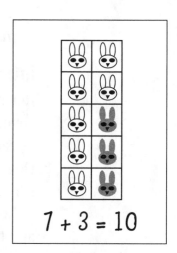

$$7 + 3 = 10$$

Once the ten-frames are complete, group all the number sentences that are the same together and have children help you organize them in a pattern: Put $0 + 10 = 10$ first, followed by $1 + 9 = 10$, and so on. With children's help determine if any number sentences are missing.

Monsters
Go to School

by _Wendy_

Monsters Go to School

pages 61–66   **SUBTRACTION**

Objective

Humorous scenes are described in which some members of a group of monsters leave the school activity in which they have been participating. With the aid of pictures and rhyming clues in the text, the children's job is to find out how many monsters are left.

Getting Started

Introduce the idea of monsters going to school. What activities would they do? Would the monsters follow classroom rules? Then present a situation similar to those in the book.

> *Suppose 6 monsters were reading books during reading time. Then 4 monsters ran outside. How many monsters would be left?*

You can put 6 tagboard monsters in a pocket chart or draw them on chart paper. Have children help you show 4 monsters leaving. (Monsters can be removed from the pocket chart or crossed out on the chart paper.) Ask how many monsters are left. Then have children create the subtraction number sentence to match the situation: 6 − 4 = 2.

Introducing the Book

Read the sample book you made and emphasize the text's rhythm and rhyme. Show children how you determined how many monsters were left in each case. Explain whether you crossed out the monsters or used rhyming clues to fill in the blank lines. Make sure children see and understand the work you did on the right-hand pages. Point out your drawings of how many monsters are left, the numbers you wrote on the blank lines, and the corresponding number sentences you completed. On the pages, make sure children realize that the first sentences begin with the numeral 1 and not the letter I.

Making the Book

Duplicate and distribute pages 61–66 to each child. Guide children through the process of assembling the mini-book. Then let them flip through the pages, noticing that the left-hand pages are drawn already, but the right-hand pages are for them to complete. Remind them that they will need to draw *how many monsters are left*, fill in the blank lines, and complete the number sentences for each two-page spread.

Sharing the Book

This is a wonderful book for children to share with partners. The context is a humorous one, and the text rhymes. The child being read to can even chime in with the rhyming word. Families will also enjoy the story. Let children share family members' comments with the whole class.

Beyond the Book

Write a new story as a class. (It doesn't have to rhyme.) Perhaps the monsters are at soccer or baseball practice, the movies, gymnastics, or the park. Use tagboard monsters with a pocket chart to act out the new class story.

Measuring Prints

pages 67–72   **MEASUREMENT**

Objective

Children measure animal tracks using the width of their thumbs, record the nonstandard measurements they find, and make comparisons. They also draw, measure, and record the length of their own handprints.

Getting Started

Ask children to talk about their experiences with measuring:

> *Who measures your height?* (doctor) *Who measures your feet?* (shoe store clerk) *Have you measured objects yourselves? What measuring tools have you used?*

Explain that for this mini-book they will be using a measuring tool they carry with them all the time—their thumbs! Find a small object, such as a short pencil, to measure with your own thumb width. Let children count the thumb widths along with you.

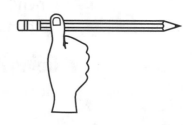

The print is 4 🖐 long.

Then turn to the subject of the mini-book—animal prints. Ask what animal prints tell you, for example, how big the animal is, that the animal lives nearby, that the animal was passing by. On chart paper, sketch a 2¾-inch bobcat pawprint like the one shown . Draw a vertical line through it. With your thumb, measure the length of the print. Let children count the thumb widths with you and write the measurement.

Introducing the Book

Read and display your completed mini-book to children. Show how you traced your thumb on page 1. Talk about how you measured the prints with your thumb by measuring along the line drawn through the print. Explain that you looked at the cover of the mini-book to help you draw pictures of the animals.

Making the Book

Duplicate and pass out pages 67–72 to each child. Guide children as they put the mini-books together. Flip through them as a class, noting the following tasks that need to be done: measuring and recording the length of the print in thumb widths and drawing each animal. Note that on page 1 they need to trace their own thumbs. On the last page, point out that children will be deciding which are the shortest and longest prints they measured.

Sharing the Book

Let children take turns reading aloud their books and sharing their measurements and animal pictures. Then ask them to compare results from the last page. (The dog print is the shortest. The handprint is the longest.)

Families will enjoy this informative mini-book. Send the books home for children to read and share. Families could even measure a pet's print in thumb widths or inches and send back the results.

Going Beyond the Book

Measure children's footprints. This can be done using wet feet or painted feet, or by having children measure their shoes. Provide connecting cubes for children to use as measuring tools. Make sure everyone uses the same unit of measure. Then compare footprints. Who has the shortest and the longest footprints?

On the Road with Dad

pages 73–78   **MONEY**

Objective

At each stop along the highway, children are given the opportunity to buy two items and to use addition to figure out the total cost. In some cases, they are told how much money they have to spend, and they find not only the total cost but also how much money is left.

Getting Started

Let children relate their shopping experiences:

> *At what kinds of stores do you like to shop?*
> *What kinds of things or foods do you like to buy?*

Pass out play pennies (give 12¢ to each child or pair of children). On chart paper, draw some objects and their prices.

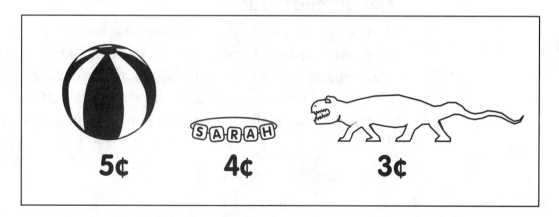

Let the class choose two items to buy. Have them use their pennies to decide how much the two items would cost together. Then choose two different items. Ask children to figure out how much these items would cost together. In this case, challenge them to tell how much money they would have left over. Talk about the cents (¢) symbol.

Introducing the Book

Explain that the girl is on a road trip with her dad. Ask if children have ever stopped at a store along a highway to buy food or other goods. Share your completed book with children. Point out how you circled the items you decided to buy on the left-hand pages and how you filled in the blank lines on the right-hand pages.

Making the Book

Duplicate and distribute pages 73–78 to each child. Help children assemble their mini-books. Go over each page together and decide what needs to be done. Consider letting children use pennies to help them fill in the blanks. They will need 12¢ each to complete all the activities. Point out that on some pages they will need to find out the total cost *and* how much money is left. In all cases, they will need to write in the cents sign.

Sharing the Book

Have children take turns reading two pages of the book in front of the class and explaining what they bought. Ask how many children bought the same two items.

When children take the book home to share with their families, encourage them to ask family members which items they would buy.

Going Beyond the Book

Set up a "highway store" in the classroom. Let children draw store items on tagboard cards and label them. Instruct them to put prices on the cards, ranging from 1¢ to 7¢ (or higher, if appropriate). Then give each child 10 to 12 pennies to spend at the store. Have children share what they bought, the total price, and how much money is left over.

Bunny's Day

pages 79–83   TIME

Objective

Children follow Bunny through the day, from the time the rabbit gets up to the time it goes to bed. They read a clock pictured on the page and complete the text that describes what Bunny is doing at each time.

Getting Started

Talk about important times in every child's day. Ask children what time they wake up and what time they go to school. Record some responses and show some of the times on a clockface. When writing the times, focus children's attention on the notation used to write time (2:00 or 2 o'clock). Go on to discuss what time recess is and what time they eat lunch and dinner. Then talk about bedtime routines and what time they go to bed. Children will discover that there is a similar pattern to most of their weekdays, with regard to time.

Introducing the Book

Introduce Bunny, the endearing character in this mini-book. Read your sample mini-book and show the drawings you made in it. Explain how you read Bunny's clock in the right-hand corner of each page and recorded the time on the blank line. Point out how you completed the sentences from page 3 on. Note that on page 7 of the book, you might want to write the title of a book, which will encourage children to do so as well.

Making the Book

After copying and passing out pages 79–83, work together to assemble the mini-books. Point out that Bunny's clock is shown in the upper right corner of each page. Review the steps for each page: Fill in the time, complete the sentence, and draw a picture.

Sharing the Book

This is a lovely book to share because children's illustrations and written responses will undoubtedly be charming. Also let children take their books home to read to family members and to gather comments. Have children notice whether parents have digital watches or watches with hands.

Going Beyond the Book

Let children make their own books using another animal as the main character but making it more realistic. For instance, a snake or a spider might have an interesting daily schedule. These books should be from 4 to 6 pages long.

Ready for Recess

pages 84–87   FRACTIONS

Objective

Children illustrate a story that reinforces the concept of *one half*. Given clues in each rhyming verse, they draw a specific set of objects and color half of the objects one color and half another color.

Getting Started

Encourage children to talk about the activities they like best at recess. Then ask about their favorite snacks to eat at the beginning of recess. How many bring apples? How many bring crackers or cookies? What other snacks do they bring? Work together to complete the verse below, which is similar to those in the mini-book:

> *6 big hula hoops*
> *shiny and new,*
> *½ of them are yellow,*
> *½ of them are blue.*

Read the verse, and ask what ½ means. Then draw 6 hula hoops on chart paper. Challenge children to think of ways to color half of them yellow and half of them blue. Try a few of the suggestions. Possible strategies are listed below:

✤ Draw 6 hoops. By guessing and checking, use a pencil to try to circle two groups with the same number of hoops in each group.

✤ Color one hoop yellow and then color one hoop blue. Keep coloring until all the hoops are colored.

❀ Draw two circles. Label them circle 1 and circle 2. Draw one hoop in circle 1 and one hoop in circle 2. Keep drawing until you have 6 hoops. (Or draw them in two rows.)

❀ Use yellow and blue cubes. Guess and check to make a group of 6 cubes that are half yellow and half blue.

❀ Have paper circles available to represent the hoops. Let children line them up in two rows and color half yellow, half blue.

❀ Ask children about the "doubles" addition facts: *What number can you double to make 6?*

Introducing the Book

Show children your own mini-book as a sample. Read the book and describe the strategies you used to color ½ one color and ½ another color. Ask children what clues are given on each page—the number of objects and the colors. Then focus on the last page, which is a little different from the previous pages. Explain that any number of children can be drawn, but half must be girls and half must be boys.

Making the Book

Copy pages 84–87 and pass out one set to each child. Let children flip through the mini-books to find the blank lines in the text and to realize that they are responsible for all illustrations. In this book, the coloring is inherent to the math.

Sharing the Book

Let pairs read their books to each other so that everyone's mathematical and artistic skills can be admired. As a class, have children share the strategies they used to color the objects.

Send the books home to be read and discussed with family members. When the books are returned to class, set aside time to read some of the comments to children.

Going Beyond the Book

Present a challenge such as the following: *Is our class half girls and half boys?* Let children find strategies to prove their answers rather than just answering yes or no. Some may suggest counting. Some may suggest physically lining up in two rows, side by side, and seeing if the rows are equal. Try this with other challenges, such as: *Does half the class have tie shoes and the other half have non-tie shoes?*

100th Day of School

pages 88–93   PLACE VALUE

Objective

On each page, children draw a different set of 10 designated objects. They also record how many objects in all they have drawn so far, which involves counting by tens. By the last page, the children will have drawn 100 objects.

Getting Started

This activity is perfect for the hundredth day of school festivities, but it can also be used when you are focusing on counting by tens or place value. For younger children, have five children come forward and put up their hands to show their fingers.

Let the rest of the children estimate how many fingers in all. Record results on the board. Then ask how many fingers each child has. With the children, count the fingers by tens to get 50. Next, bring five more children to the front of the room. Have the rest of the children estimate how many fingers there are now. With the children, count by tens to get 100.

An alternative for older children is to ask how many children you'd need to bring forward to have 50 fingers and 100 fingers.

Introducing the Book

Have a finished book ready to show the class. On the first three pages, count the 10 bugs, the 10 snakes, and the 10 leaves. Be sure to explain what is happening at the bottom of each page, where a child is counting by tens to keep track of how many objects there are in all.

Making the Book

Make copies of pages 88–93 and give one set to each child. Assemble the mini-books with children. Review the steps for each page: Draw 10 objects and record how many in all in the speech balloon at the bottom of the page. Remind children that they should draw a picture of themselves on page 10.

Sharing the Book

Let partners take turns reading the book to each other and showing the pictures they drew. Then read the book in unison with the class, saying the cumulative number of objects louder than the rest of the text.

Send the mini-book home to be shared with family members. When the books are returned with comments, put them on a special "100th Day of School" display table.

Going Beyond the Book

Use the mini-book as a springboard for a class activity related to the 100th day of school. Children can either bring in collections of 10 or collections of 100. They may use zip-lock bags or glue the items to tagboard.

_____
date

Dear Family,

Our class is making mini-books this year to learn mathematics, reading, and writing, all at the same time.

Each book has a story that teaches a different math concept, and the books are written in a way that makes them easy to read. The children are very excited and proud of the books they made and would like to share them with you. Thank you for taking the time to let your child read the book to you and talk about it with you.

You'll notice a page for comments at the back of each book. This space is for you to write supportive comments about the book and about your child's presentation of the book. You can comment on the way your child read, the illustrations, the math, the writing, or your child's enthusiasm and improvement. You might also want to comment on how your child understands and explains math ideas, writes numbers clearly, sounds out words, recognizes words without sounding them out, reads with expression, and has improved in math, reading, and writing. Please return the mini-books to the classroom by _____.

Thank you for helping with this project. Your child values your support very much.

                                        Sincerely,

_____

12 Reproducible Write-and-Read Math Story Books Scholastic Professional Books

12 Write-and-Read Math Story Books

A Hat for Each Head — by Hector

The Circus — by Benny

At the Pond — by Sally

I Like Shapes — square, circle, triangle, restangle — by James

The Elves Have a Tea Party — by Maria

Making 10 with Mr. Bear — by Lee

Monsters Go to School — by Wendy

Measuring Prints — by Ryan

On the Road with Dad — by Sarah

Bunny's Day — by Lisa

Ready for Recess — by Sam

100th Day of School — HAPPY 100th DAY! — by Maxie

Comments

A Hat for Each Head

by _____

Write-and-Read Math Story Books Scholastic Professional Books

2 clowns have hats.

2 clowns have _____ hats.

1

4 workers have hats.

4 workers have _____ hats.

2

3 baseball players have hats.

3 baseball players have

_____ hats.

2 bike riders have hats.

2 bike riders have _____ hats.

Write-and-Read Math Story Books Scholastic Professional Books

3 firefighters have hats.

3 firefighters have _____ hats.

5 children have silly hats.

5 children have _____ hats.

Comments

The Circus

Write-and-Read Math Story Books Scholastic Professional Books

by _____

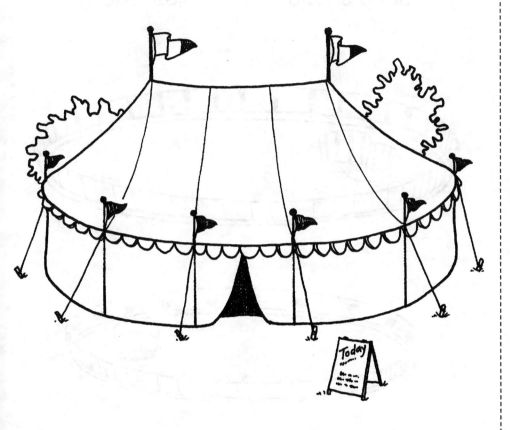

There is _____ tent.

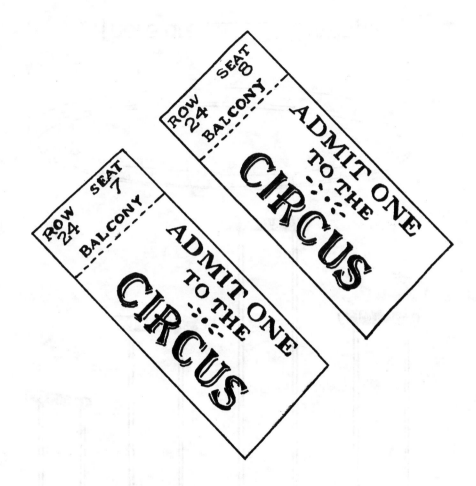

There are _____ tickets.

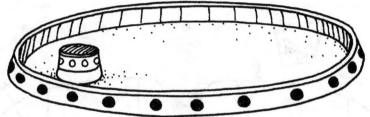
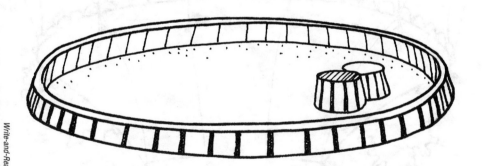

There are _____ circus rings.

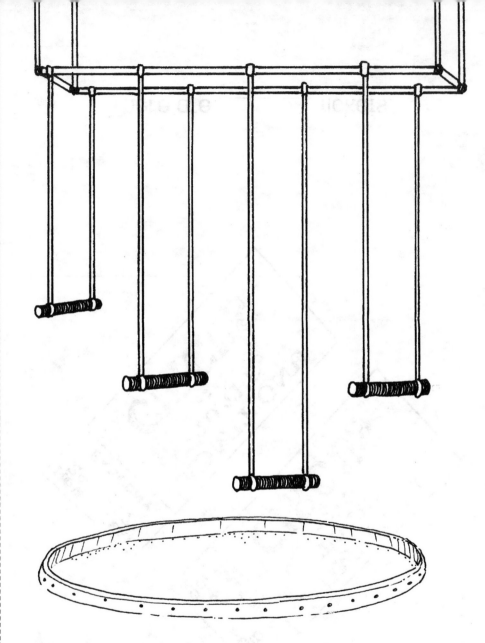

There are _____ swings.

There are _____ elephants.

There are _____ lions.

There are _____ dogs.

7

There are _____ balloons.

8

There are _____ balls.

9

There are _____ circus clowns!

10

Comments

At the Pond

Write-and-Read Math Story Books Scholastic Professional Books

by _____

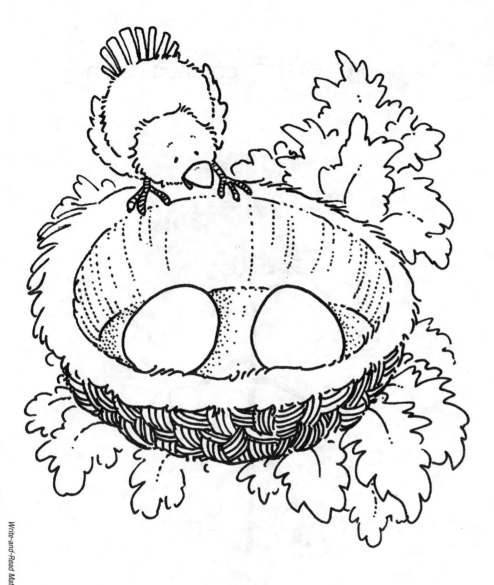

The bird counted _____ eggs.

The frog counted _____ flies.

1

2

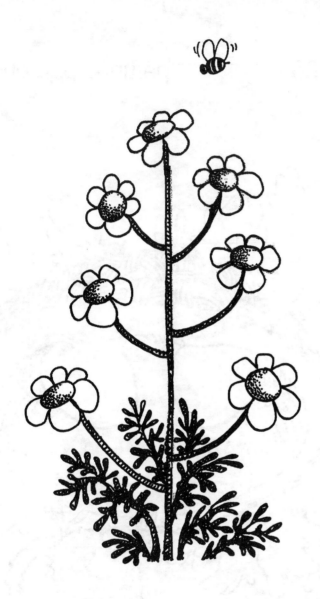

The bee counted _____ flowers.

The mouse counted _____ berries.

The fish counted _____ bubbles.

5

The squirrel counted _____ nuts.

6

The turtle counted _____ rocks.

7

The dog counted _____ balls.

8

A house is squares and a triangle.

A car is rectangles and circles.

Comments

The Elves Have a Tea Party

by _____

Write-and-Read Math Story Books Scholastic Professional Books

Franny has 2 mint leaves.
Freddy has 3 mint leaves.

2 + 3 = _____

Franny has 3 toadstools.
Freddy has 4 toadstools.

_____

Franny has 2 cups.
Freddy has 5 cups.

Franny has 5 butterflies.
Freddy has 3 butterflies.

Franny has 4 flowers.
Freddy has 2 flowers.

5

All their elf friends come to visit.
It's time for the tea party!

6

Comments

Write-and-Read Math Story Books Scholastic Professional Books

Making 10 with Mr. Bear

by _____

Here is Mr. Bear.
He loves to make 10 with me.

1

We plant 10 flowers.

Mr. Bear plants 7 flowers.

I plant _____ flowers.

2

We plant 10 flowers.

$$7 + \rule{2cm}{0.4pt} = 10$$

3

We bake 10 cookies.

Mr. Bear bakes 4 cookies.

I bake _____ cookies.

4

We bake 10 cookies.

$$4 + \underline{\hspace{2cm}} = 10$$

We buy 10 stickers.

Mr. Bear buys _____ stickers.

I buy _____ stickers.

We buy 10 stickers.

$$8 + \underline{\hspace{2cm}} = 10$$

Write-and-Read Math Story Books Scholastic Professional Books

We take 10 photos.

Mr. Bear takes _____ photos.

I take _____ photos.

We take 10 photos.

5 + _____ = 10

We draw 10 hearts.

Mr. Bear draws _____ heart.

I draw _____ hearts.

We draw 10 hearts.

$1 +$ _____ $= 10$

We found ways of making ten.
Let's play with Mr. Bear again!

Comments

Write-and-Read Math Story Books Scholastic Professional Books

Monsters
Go to School

by _____

9 little monsters
went to school in fall.
Count the little monsters,
one and all.

1

9 little monsters
walked in the door.

2

Draw 4.

5 ran and hid,
and then there were _____.

$9 - 5 = \underline{\quad 4 \quad}$

6 little monsters
tying their shoes,

Write-and-Read Math Story Books Scholastic Professional Books

4 went out to play,
and then there were _____.

6 – 4 = _____

7 little monsters
playing with sticks.

I fell asleep,
and then there were _____.

$$7 - 1 = \text{_____}$$

9 little monsters
having lots of fun.

8 went home,
and then there was _____.

$$9 - 8 = \text{_____}$$

9

I little monster
playing in the sun.
She ran home,
and then there were n __ __ __.

$$I - I = \text{_____}$$

10

Comments

Measuring Prints

Write-and-Read Math Story Books Scholastic Professional Books

by _____

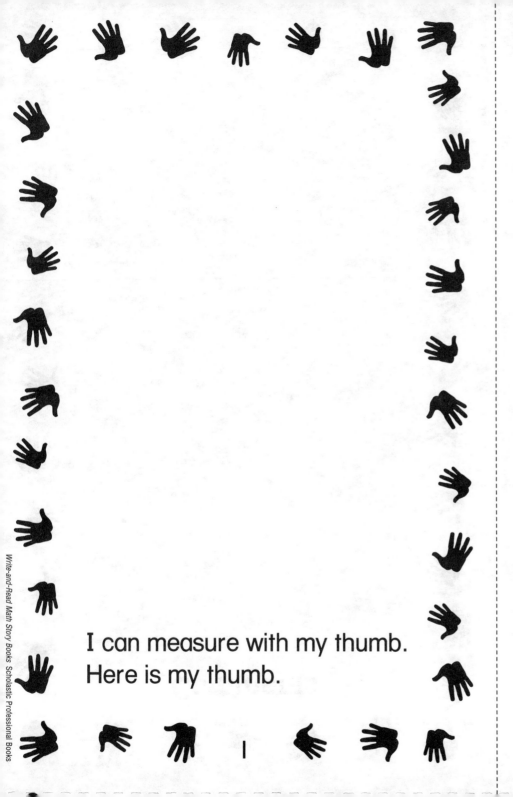

I can measure with my thumb.
Here is my thumb.

1

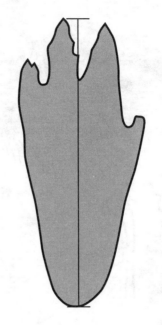

I measured the rabbit print.

It is _____ long.

2

Here is the rabbit.

Write-and-Read Math Story Books Scholastic Professional Books

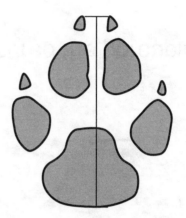

I measured the dog print.

It is _____ long.

Here is the dog.

Write-and-Read Math Story Books Scholastic Professional Books

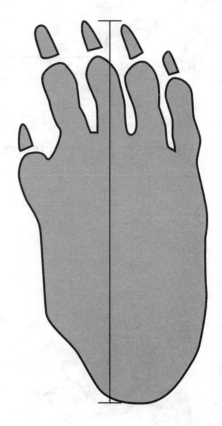

I measured the porcupine print.

It is _____ long.

Here is the porcupine.

7

I measured my handprint.

It is _____ long.

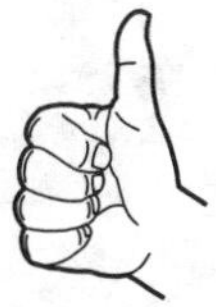

8

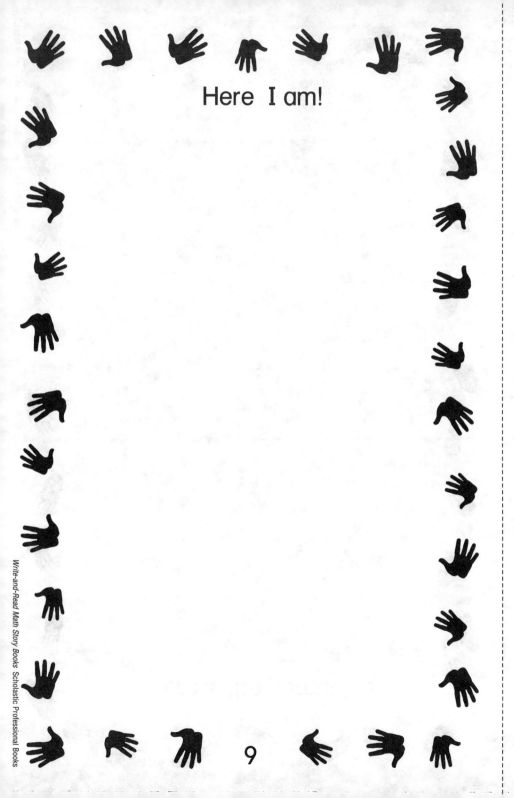

Here I am!

Write-and-Read Math Story Books Scholastic Professional Books

I measured with my thumb.

The _____ print was the shortest.

The _____ print was the longest!

Comments

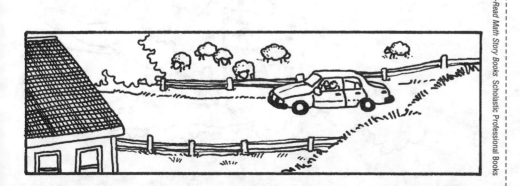

Write-and-Read Math Story Books Scholastic Professional Books

On the Road with Dad

by _____

Dad and I went on a trip.
We drove in the car.

1

Farm Stand

grapes
5¢

peanuts
4¢

raisins
2¢

2

At the first stop,

I bought _____

and _____.

They cost _____ ¢.

Stop 2

At the second stop,

I bought a _____

and a _____.

They cost _____¢.

Stop 3

trail mix   7¢

crackers
4¢

popcorn
5¢

At the third stop,
I had 12¢ to spend.

I bought _____

and _____ .

They cost _____ .

I had _____ left.

Write-and-Read Math Story Books   Scholastic Professional Books

Last Stop

At the last stop,
I had 12¢ to spend.

I bought a _____ cone

and a _____ cone.

They cost _____.

I had _____ left.

I like to go on trips with Dad.
We have fun on the road.

Comments

Bunny's Day

by _____

It is _____.

Bunny wakes up.

It is _____.

Bunny goes to school.

Write-and-Read Math Story Books Scholastic Professional Books

It is _____.

Bunny likes to play _____
at recess.

It is _____.

Bunny likes to eat _____
for lunch.

It is _____.

Bunny likes to play _____ after school.

It is _____ at night.

Bunny likes to eat _____ for dinner.

5

6

It is _____ at night.

Bunny's mom reads

_____

to Bunny.

7

It is _____ at night.

Bunny goes _____.

8

Write-and-Read Math Story Books Scholastic Professional Books

Comments

Ready for Recess

6 shiny marbles,

I'll give you a clue,

$\frac{1}{2}$ of them are red,

$\frac{1}{2}$ of them are _____.

1

4 yummy cookies

ready to bite,

$\frac{1}{2}$ of them are brown,

$\frac{1}{2}$ of them are _____.

2

10 long jump ropes,

turning round and round,

$\frac{1}{2}$ of them are purple,

$\frac{1}{2}$ of them are _____.

3

8 crunchy apples

shiny and clean,

$\frac{1}{2}$ of them are yellow,

$\frac{1}{2}$ of them are _____.

4

12 rubber balls,

bouncy and new,

$\frac{1}{2}$ of them are orange,

$\frac{1}{2}$ of them are _____.

Recess is over,

We bring in the toys,

$\frac{1}{2}$ of us are girls,

$\frac{1}{2}$ of us are boys.

Comments

Write-and-Read Math Story Books Scholastic Professional Books

100th Day of School

by _____

Benny brought in
10 red bugs,
in his daddy's water jug.

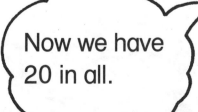

We have
10 in all.

1

Sally brought in
10 long snakes,
Teacher said, "For goodness sake!"

Now we have
20 in all.

2

Lenny brought in
10 green leaves,
from the pretty maple trees.

Now we have
30 in all.

Cassy brought in
10 white cakes,
that her Grandma Jenny makes.

Now we have
_____ in all.

Write-and-Read Math Story Books Scholastic Professional Books

Bobby brought in
10 ripe beans,
in a lovely shade of green.

Now we have

_____ in all.

Clara brought in
10 small clocks,
Tick-tock, tick-tock, tick, tick, tock.

Now we have

_____ in all.

Sammy brought in
10 brown seeds,
He can plant them once he weeds.

7

Ronny brought in
10 black rocks,
in a little yellow sock.

8

Billy brought in
10 balloons,
Counting can be fun to do.

9

Me? I brought in
10 bright balls,
That's 100 things in all!

10

About the Author

This author of this book is _____

_____.

_____ is _____ years old

and lives in _____.

The author likes to _____,

_____, and

_____.

This is a picture of the author,

_____.

Comments

by _____